Flute—Book 1

SECOND EDITION

W9-CBU-690

Desktop — Mobile
I P S
INTERACTIVE
Practice Studio
Audio — Video — Extras

smartmusic.

Tradition of Excellence™

Comprehensive Band Method

by Bruce Pearson & Ryan Nowlin

Dear Student:

Welcome to your study of the flute—an exciting adventure filled with rewards and challenges. Through careful study and regular practice, you will quickly discover the joy and satisfaction of playing beautiful music for yourself, your family, your friends, or a concert audience. We wish you many rewarding years of flute playing.

Bruce Pearson Bruce Pearson

Ryan Nowlin Ryan Nowlin

PRACTICE JOURNAL

Week	Date Assigned	Assignment/Goal	Minutes Practiced							Total Minutes	Initial
			Su	M	Tu	W	Th	F	Sa		
1											
2											
3											
4											
5											
6											
7											
8											
9											
10											
11											
12											
13											
14											
15											
16											

A full Practice Journal is available from your teacher or from your **INTERACTIVE Practice Studio**.

I P S
INTERACTIVE
Practice Studio

Enhance your practice by frequently visiting the **INTERACTIVE Practice Studio**. See the inside back cover for more information.

smartmusic.

Tradition of Excellence is available in SmartMusic. To subscribe, go to www.smartmusic.com.

ISBN 10: 0-8497-7051-3 • ISBN 13: 978-0-8497-7051-7

Tradition of Excellence and **INTERACTIVE Practice Studio** are trademarks of Kjos Music Press.

For more detailed instruction, be sure to view the Video Lessons in your *Tradition of Excellence* **INTERACTIVE Practice Studio**. Lessons are available every time you see this icon.

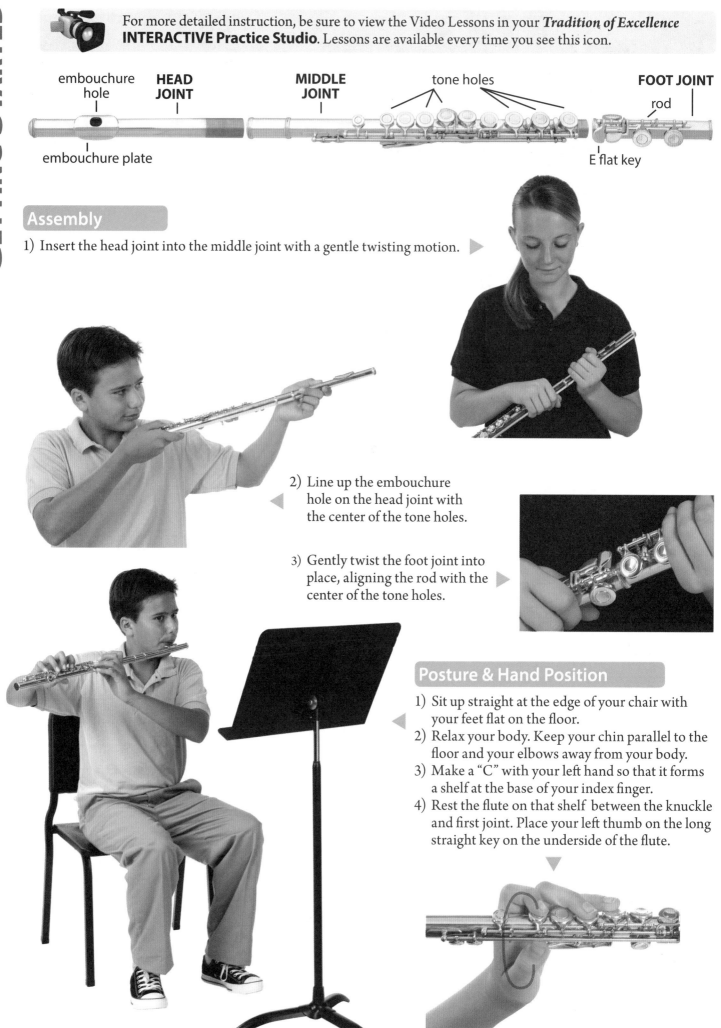

embouchure hole   **HEAD JOINT**   **MIDDLE JOINT**   tone holes   **FOOT JOINT**

rod

embouchure plate   E flat key

Assembly

1) Insert the head joint into the middle joint with a gentle twisting motion.

2) Line up the embouchure hole on the head joint with the center of the tone holes.

3) Gently twist the foot joint into place, aligning the rod with the center of the tone holes.

Posture & Hand Position

1) Sit up straight at the edge of your chair with your feet flat on the floor.
2) Relax your body. Keep your chin parallel to the floor and your elbows away from your body.
3) Make a "C" with your left hand so that it forms a shelf at the base of your index finger.
4) Rest the flute on that shelf between the knuckle and first joint. Place your left thumb on the long straight key on the underside of the flute.

5) Place the tip of your right thumb under the flute between the first and second fingers of your right hand.

6) Curve your fingers on both hands to form a relaxed "C," as if holding a tennis ball. Place your right little finger on the E flat key and your other fingers on the correct keys. Keep your right wrist as straight as possible.

Forming an Embouchure & Making a Tone

1) Remove the head joint and cover the open end.
2) Relax your face and shape your mouth as if saying "whee" while you say "too" with your lower lip drooping down slightly at the corners.
3) Place the lip plate so that the lower lip rolls out slightly and covers approximately ⅓ of the embouchure hole. Make certain the head joint is parallel to your lips.
4) Take a full breath and blow over the embouchure hole, aiming a thin stream of air at the far edge of the hole while whispering the syllable "too." Use a mirror to check your embouchure.
5) Take a full breath of air through your mouth and play a long, steady A.
6) Complete the **Head Joint Workout** by watching the video lesson and playing along with the recorded accompaniment (see the inside back cover for details).

Daily Care & Maintenance

1) Take the flute apart and shake the water out of the head joint. Wipe the joints clean.
2) Dry the inside of your flute with a soft cloth placed over a cleaning rod.
3) Wipe the outside of each part with a soft, clean cloth.
4) Each time you finish caring for a part of the flute, return it to its proper place in the case. Latch the case.

FLUTE LESSON

Terms & Symbols

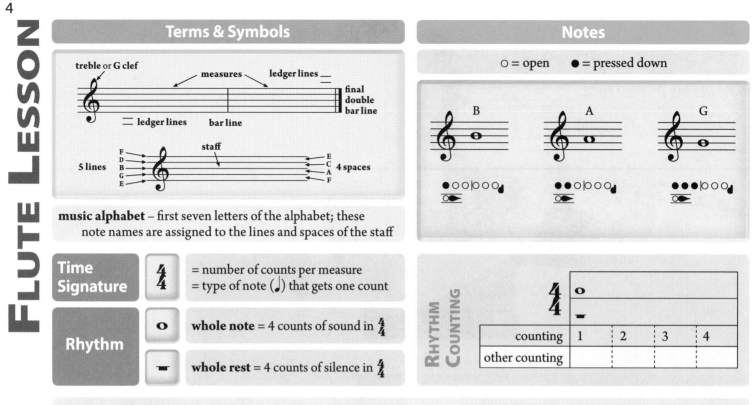

treble or G clef

measures

ledger lines

final double bar line

ledger lines

bar line

staff

5 lines

F
D
B
G
E

E
C
A
F

4 spaces

music alphabet – first seven letters of the alphabet; these note names are assigned to the lines and spaces of the staff

Time Signature

$\frac{4}{4}$ = number of counts per measure
= type of note (♩) that gets one count

Rhythm

○ **whole note** = 4 counts of sound in $\frac{4}{4}$

▬ **whole rest** = 4 counts of silence in $\frac{4}{4}$

Notes

○ = open   ● = pressed down

RHYTHM COUNTING

$\frac{4}{4}$	○			
	▬			
counting	1	2	3	4
other counting				

Use the audio, video, and extras provided in your *Tradition of Excellence* **INTERACTIVE Practice Studio** to enhance every practice session. See the inside back cover for more information.

staff & bar lines

$\frac{4}{4}$ ○ ▬

1. Busy "B"   ▸ How is your posture?

2. The "A" Train   ▸ Are you using plenty of air?

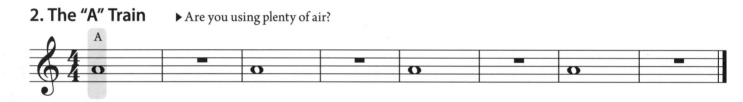

3. Music in Motion   ▸ Are you playing with a good embouchure?

4. "G" Whiz   ▸ How is your hand position?

5. Mr. Whole Note Takes a Walk   ▸ Write the note names beneath the music before you play.

WOODWIND LESSON

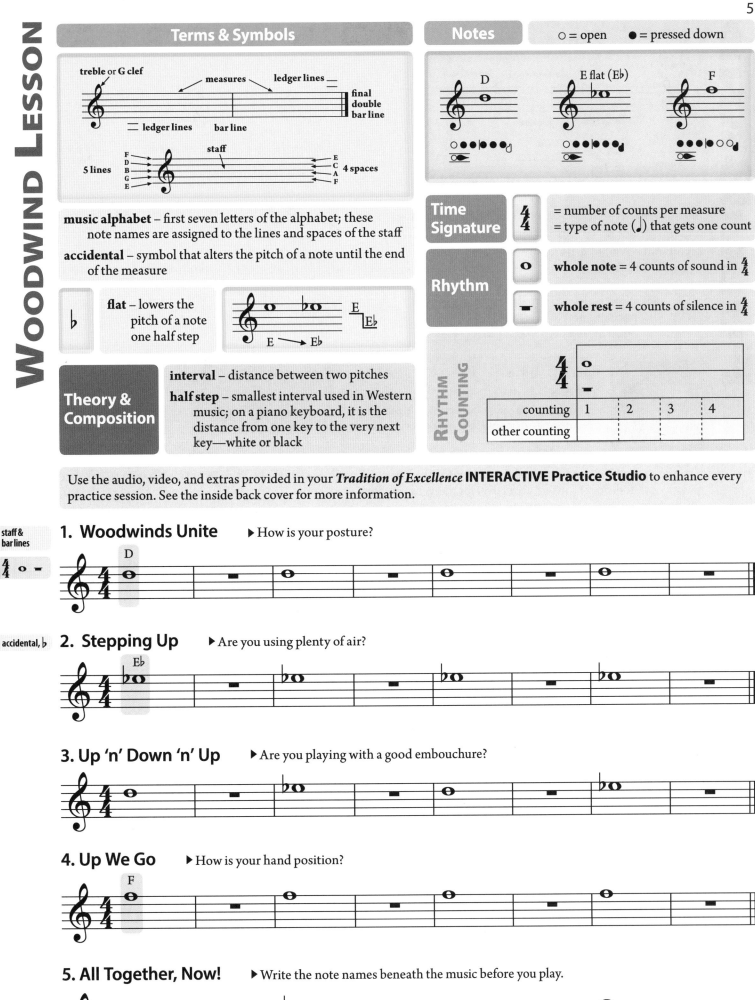

Terms & Symbols

treble or G clef
measures
ledger lines
final double bar line
ledger lines
bar line
staff
5 lines
F D B G E
E C A F
4 spaces

music alphabet – first seven letters of the alphabet; these note names are assigned to the lines and spaces of the staff

accidental – symbol that alters the pitch of a note until the end of the measure

♭ **flat** – lowers the pitch of a note one half step

E → E♭

Theory & Composition

interval – distance between two pitches

half step – smallest interval used in Western music; on a piano keyboard, it is the distance from one key to the very next key—white or black

Notes

○ = open   ● = pressed down

D   E flat (E♭)   F

Time Signature

4/4 = number of counts per measure
= type of note (♩) that gets one count

Rhythm

o **whole note** = 4 counts of sound in 4/4

▬ **whole rest** = 4 counts of silence in 4/4

RHYTHM COUNTING

4/4	o			
	▬			
counting	1	2	3	4
other counting				

Use the audio, video, and extras provided in your *Tradition of Excellence* **INTERACTIVE Practice Studio** to enhance every practice session. See the inside back cover for more information.

staff & bar lines

1. Woodwinds Unite ▸ How is your posture?

accidental, ♭

2. Stepping Up ▸ Are you using plenty of air?

3. Up 'n' Down 'n' Up ▸ Are you playing with a good embouchure?

4. Up We Go ▸ How is your hand position?

5. All Together, Now! ▸ Write the note names beneath the music before you play.

W61FL

FULL BAND

Terms & Symbols

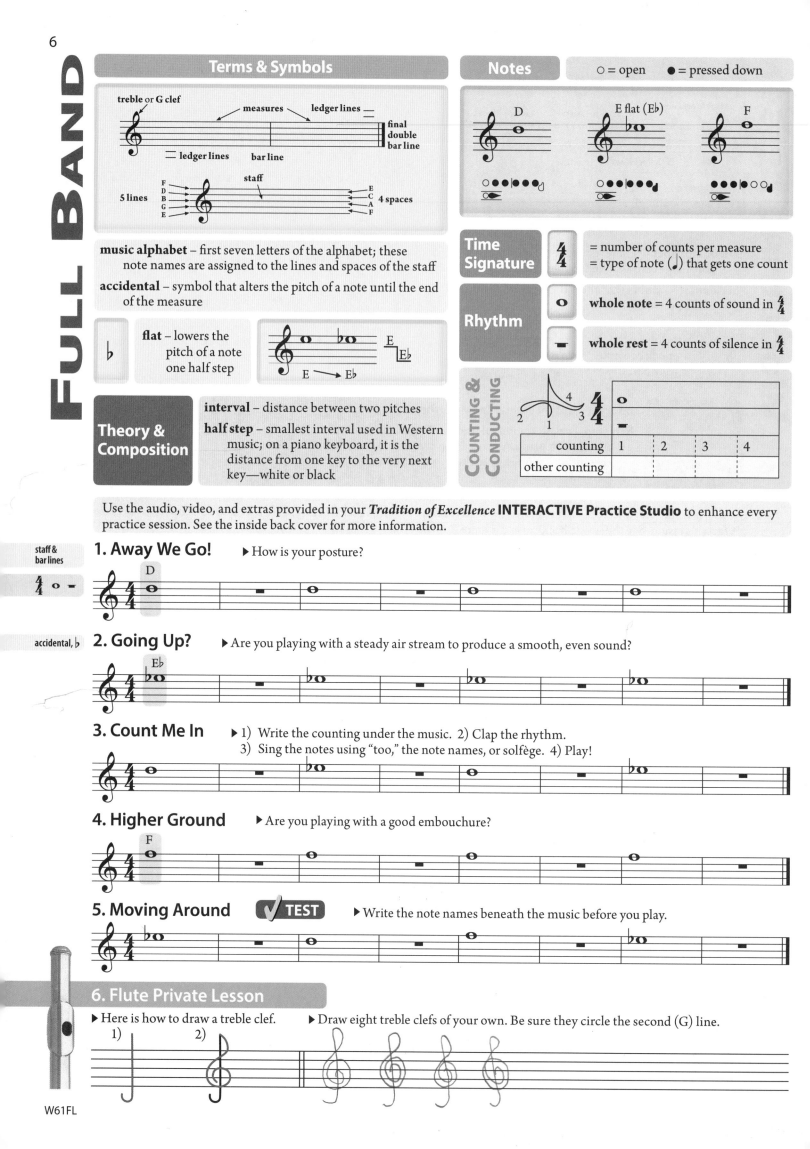

5 lines   F D B G E   staff   E C A F   4 spaces

music alphabet – first seven letters of the alphabet; these note names are assigned to the lines and spaces of the staff

accidental – symbol that alters the pitch of a note until the end of the measure

♭ **flat** – lowers the pitch of a note one half step

E → E♭

Theory & Composition

interval – distance between two pitches

half step – smallest interval used in Western music; on a piano keyboard, it is the distance from one key to the very next key—white or black

Notes

○ = open   ● = pressed down

D   E flat (E♭)   F

Time Signature   4/4   = number of counts per measure
= type of note (♩) that gets one count

Rhythm   ○   **whole note** = 4 counts of sound in 4/4

—   **whole rest** = 4 counts of silence in 4/4

COUNTING & CONDUCTING

		counting	1	2	3	4
	other counting					

Use the audio, video, and extras provided in your *Tradition of Excellence* **INTERACTIVE Practice Studio** to enhance every practice session. See the inside back cover for more information.

staff & bar lines

4/4 ○ —

1. Away We Go!   ▶ How is your posture?

D

accidental, ♭

2. Going Up?   ▶ Are you playing with a steady air stream to produce a smooth, even sound?

E♭

3. Count Me In   ▶ 1) Write the counting under the music. 2) Clap the rhythm.
3) Sing the notes using "too," the note names, or solfège. 4) Play!

4. Higher Ground   ▶ Are you playing with a good embouchure?

F

5. Moving Around   ✓ **TEST**   ▶ Write the note names beneath the music before you play.

6. Flute Private Lesson

▶ Here is how to draw a treble clef.   ▶ Draw eight treble clefs of your own. Be sure they circle the second (G) line.

1)   2)

Terms & Symbols

,   **breath mark** – take a breath

sight-reading – playing or singing a piece of music for the first time

Theory & Composition

duet – piece of music featuring two different parts played or sung together

harmony – two or more notes played or sung at the same time

Rhythm

half note = 2 counts of sound in 4/4

half rest = 2 counts of silence in 4/4

COUNTING & CONDUCTING

	counting	1	2	3	4
	other counting				

7. Deep Breaths

8. Rhythm Time
▶ 1) Write the counting and clap the rhythm before you play. 2) Play on the note D (Concert D).

RHYTHM STUDIES: p. 44, #1-4

9. Half Note Rock

10. *Sight-Reading Challenge:* **Steppin'**
▶ Always carefully inspect music before you sight-read it.

11. El Camino Mariachi — *Duet*
▶ Count, clap, sing, and play! The B part is shaded for easier reading.

A.

B.

12. Cuckoo ✓ TEST
Traditional

13. Excellence in Ear Training
▶ Practice with the recorded accompaniment. Listen in measures 1, 3, 5, and 7. In measures 2, 4, 6, and 8, echo what you heard. Your starting notes are shown.

1 Listen   2 Play   3 Listen   4 Play   5 Listen   6 Play   7 Listen   8 Play

Rhythm

quarter note = 1 count of sound in $\frac{4}{4}$

quarter rest = 1 count of silence in $\frac{4}{4}$

COUNTING & CONDUCTING

counting	1	2	3	4
other counting				

Notes

C   B flat (B♭)

14. Rhythm Time
▶ 1) Write the counting and clap the rhythm before you play. 2) Play on the note D (Concert D).

RHYTHM STUDIES: p. 44, #5-17

15. Rising Rhythms
▶ Start each note by whispering the word "too."

16. Stepping Stones
▶ Keep the air moving.

17. Rain, Rain
▶ Be sure fingers not in use remain very close to the keys.

Traditional

18. In a Minor Mood
▶ Count, clap, sing, and play!

19. Hot Cross Buns
English Folk Song

20. Go Tell Aunt Rhodie
✓ TEST
American Folk Song

21. Flute Private Lesson
▶ 1) Draw a treble clef at the beginning of the staff.
2) Trace the notes, accidental, and rests, and draw three more of each.

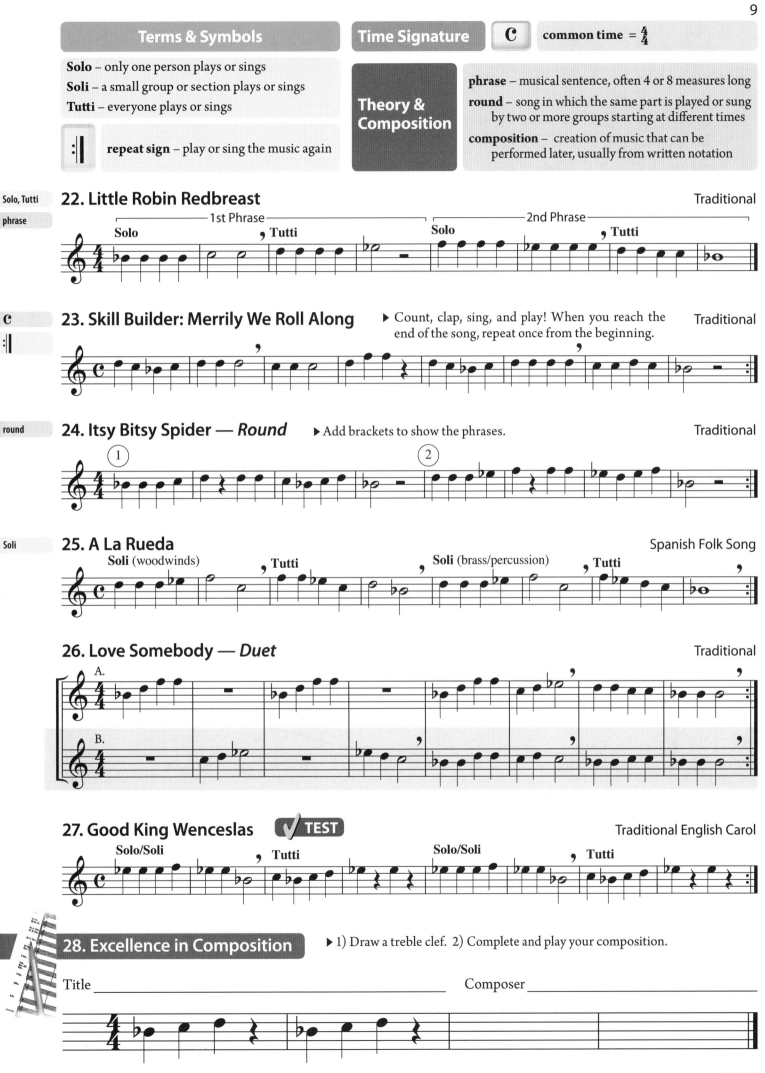

Terms & Symbols

Solo – only one person plays or sings
Soli – a small group or section plays or sings
Tutti – everyone plays or sings

repeat sign – play or sing the music again

Time Signature C common time = 4/4

Theory & Composition

phrase – musical sentence, often 4 or 8 measures long
round – song in which the same part is played or sung by two or more groups starting at different times
composition – creation of music that can be performed later, usually from written notation

Solo, Tutti
phrase

22. Little Robin Redbreast
Traditional

1st Phrase — 2nd Phrase

Solo Tutti Solo Tutti

C

23. Skill Builder: Merrily We Roll Along
▶ Count, clap, sing, and play! When you reach the end of the song, repeat once from the beginning.
Traditional

round

24. Itsy Bitsy Spider — *Round*
▶ Add brackets to show the phrases.
Traditional

Soli

25. A La Rueda
Spanish Folk Song

Soli (woodwinds) Tutti Soli (brass/percussion) Tutti

26. Love Somebody — *Duet*
Traditional

A.

B.

27. Good King Wenceslas ✓ TEST
Traditional English Carol

Solo/Soli Tutti Solo/Soli Tutti

28. Excellence in Composition
▶ 1) Draw a treble clef. 2) Complete and play your composition.

Title _____ Composer _____

10

Terms & Symbols

articulation – type of attack used to play a note or group of notes

slur – articulation that connects notes of *different* pitches; indicates a very smooth sound with only the first note tongued

Notes

G

one-measure repeat sign – play or sing the previous measure again

slur

29. Warm-up: Serenity — *Round*   ▶ Keep the air moving.

① ② ③

30. Chop Builder   ▶ Be sure fingers not in use remain very close to the keys.

G

31. Camptown Races   ▶ Draw the missing notes in the ovals before you play.

Stephen Foster, America's first great popular songwriter, was born on the 50th anniversary of American Independence: the Fourth of July, 1826.

Stephen Foster
(1826–1864)
American Composer

Solo/Soli   Tutti   Solo/Soli   Tutti

32. Skill Builder   ▶ Add brackets to show the phrases.

33. London Bridge — *Duet*   English Folk Song

A.

B.

34. The Frog's Song — *Round*   ✓ TEST   ▶ Are you using a steady air stream?   Japanese Folk Song

① ②

35. Flute Private Lesson   ▶ Keep your fingers close to the keys.

||||| **MASTERING EXCELLENCE:** p. 38, #1 ➡

Time Signature

2/4 = two counts per measure
= quarter note gets one count

COUNTING & CONDUCTING

| | counting | 1 | 2 |
| | other counting | | |

Rhythm

tie – marking that connects notes of the *same* pitch to make one longer note

Notes

Key Signature

sharp (♯) or flat (♭) signs placed after a clef

In these key signatures, play or sing:
- no sharps or flats
- every F as F sharp
- every B as B flat
- every B as B flat, every E as E flat

---

tie, 2/4

36. Rhythm Time
▶ 1) Write the counting and clap the rhythm before you play. 2) Play on the note C (Concert C).

RHYTHM STUDIES: p. 44, #18-20; p. 46, #41-43

---

key signature

37. Two Step
▶ Circle the notes changed by the B♭ major (Concert B♭ major) key signature, highlighted in purple.

---

38. *Sight-Reading Challenge:* Shoo Fly
American Folk Song

---

39. Russian Folk Song — *Duet*
Beethoven bridged music history's Classical and Romantic Periods.

Ludwig van Beethoven (1770–1827)
German Composer

A.

B.

---

40. San Serení ✓ TEST
▶ Add brackets to show the phrases.

Puerto Rican Folk Song

---

41. Excellence in Theory
▶ Add the notes and rests together to find the number of counts. A quarter note gets one count.

a) ♩ + ♩ = ___

b) ♩ + ♩ = ___

c) 𝄽 + ♩ + ▬ = ___

d) 𝅝 + ▬ = ___

ENSEMBLES

Theory & Composition	Terms & Symbols
trio – piece of music featuring three different parts played or sung together	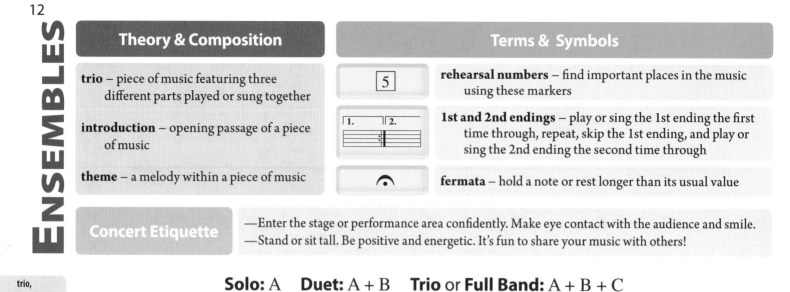 **rehearsal numbers** – find important places in the music using these markers
introduction – opening passage of a piece of music	**1st and 2nd endings** – play or sing the 1st ending the first time through, repeat, skip the 1st ending, and play or sing the 2nd ending the second time through
theme – a melody within a piece of music	**fermata** – hold a note or rest longer than its usual value

Concert Etiquette

—Enter the stage or performance area confidently. Make eye contact with the audience and smile.
—Stand or sit tall. Be positive and energetic. It's fun to share your music with others!

trio,
introduction,
theme

rehearsal
numbers,
1st & 2nd
endings

Solo: A   **Duet:** A + B   **Trio** or **Full Band:** A + B + C

Jingle Bells

J.S. Pierpont (1822–1893)
American Composer

▶ Repeat back to 5 .

Jolly Old St. Nicholas

Traditional

W61FL

The Dreidel Song

Jewish Folk Song

Kwanzaa Celebration

David Bobrowitz (b. 1945)
American Composer

14

Rhythm

eighth note = ½ count of sound
in ¾, ⁴⁄₄, or **C**

a single eighth note has a **flag**

a group of eighth notes is connected by
a **beam**

COUNTING & CONDUCTING

42. Warm-up: Breath Support Challenge ▸ Take a deep breath and play with your best tone while holding the pitch for as long as you can. On which beat did you finish?

43. Epic Eighth Notes ▸ The bottom line provides the basic pulse.

44. Michael Finnegan ▸ Count, clap, sing, and play!   Irish Folk Song

45. Eighth Note Escapade

46. Skill Builder: Processional Dance ▸ Count, clap, sing, and play!   Renaissance Dance Music

47. Baja Breeze ✓ TEST

48. Flute Private Lesson ▸ 1) Write the note names. 2) Fill in the fingering chart for each note.

W61FL

Theory & Composition   **improvisation** – spontaneous composition of music through playing or singing

49. Unforgettable Eighth Notes

50. Mahnomen Harvest   ▶ Count, clap, sing, and play!

51. Eighth Notes on the Edge

52. Now Let Me Fly   ▶ Count, clap, sing, and play!

Spirituals are religious folk songs created in the 18th and 19th centuries.   American Spiritual

53. *Sight-Reading Challenge:* Promenade   ▶ 1) Write the counting and draw the bar lines. 2) Sight-read!

54. Rio Con Brio   ✓ TEST

55. Excellence in Improvisation   ▶ Play along with the recorded accompaniment. Measures 1-2: Play the written notes. Measures 3-5: Improvise using the same notes.

Rhythm

pick-up or **anacrusis** – music that comes before the first full measure; rhythmic value of the pick-up is sometimes removed from the last measure

Notes

A flat (A♭)

Key Signature

E♭ major (Concert E♭ major) – play or sing every B as B♭, E as E♭, A as A♭

Theory & Composition

theme and variation – type of composition that begins with a main melody (**theme**) and continues with different versions (**variations**) of the main melody

56. Warm-up: Chorale — *Duet*

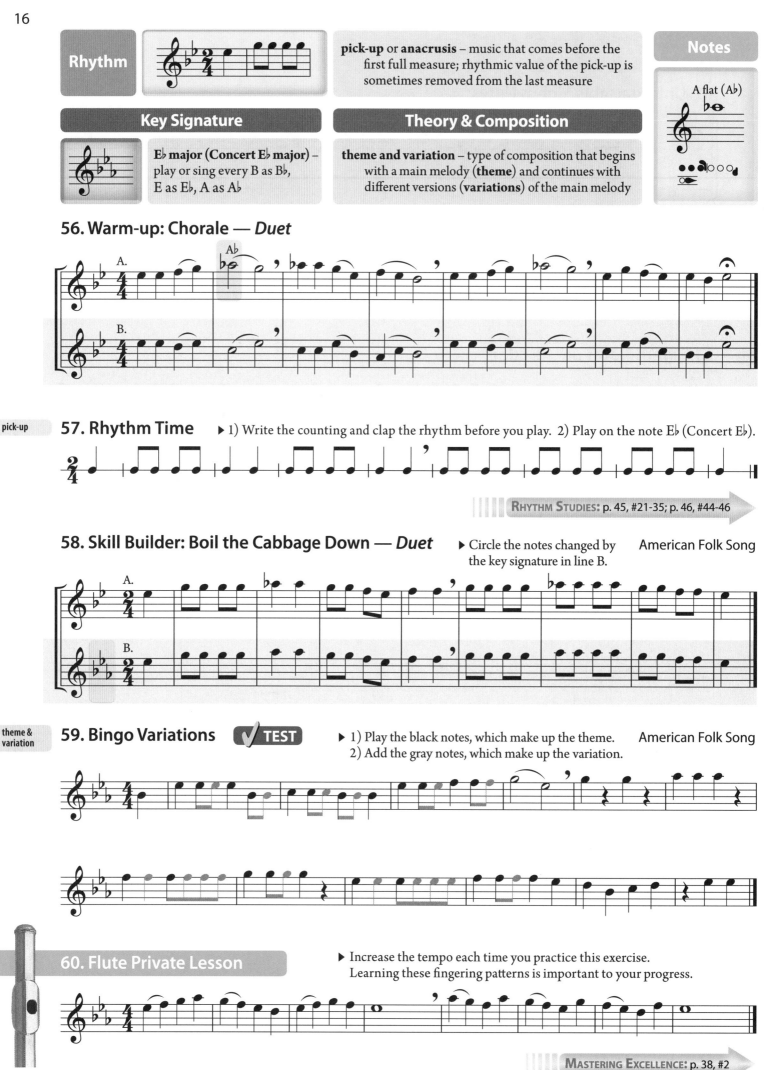

pick-up

57. Rhythm Time

▶ 1) Write the counting and clap the rhythm before you play. 2) Play on the note E♭ (Concert E♭).

RHYTHM STUDIES: p. 45, #21-35; p. 46, #44-46

58. Skill Builder: Boil the Cabbage Down — *Duet*

▶ Circle the notes changed by the key signature in line B.

American Folk Song

theme & variation

59. Bingo Variations　✓ TEST

▶ 1) Play the black notes, which make up the theme. 2) Add the gray notes, which make up the variation.

American Folk Song

60. Flute Private Lesson

▶ Increase the tempo each time you practice this exercise. Learning these fingering patterns is important to your progress.

MASTERING EXCELLENCE: p. 38, #2

Rhythm

. **dot** – adds half the value of the note

$$\text{d. } = \text{d } + \text{ } = \text{d.}$$
$$2 + 1 = 2 + 1 = 3$$

dotted half note = 3 counts of sound in $\frac{3}{4}$, $\frac{4}{4}$, or **C**

Time Signature

$\frac{3}{4}$ = three counts per measure
= quarter note gets one count

COUNTING & CONDUCTING

			counting	1 &	2 &	3 &
			other counting			

Terms & Symbols

dynamics – softness or loudness of a piece of music

p **piano** – soft

f **forte** – loud

61. Rhythm Time
▶ 1) Write the counting and clap the rhythm before you play. 2) Play on the note E♭ (Concert E♭).

RHYTHM STUDIES: p. 46, #49-53

62. Encounter in Three
▶ Circle the notes changed by the key signature.

63. Skill Builder: A Simple Waltz

64. *Sight-Reading Challenge:* Theme from "Cambridge Overture"

Anne McGinty is one of the most prolific female composers of band music and has over 225 pieces published for band, orchestra, and flute.

Anne McGinty (b. 1945)
American Composer

From *Cambridge Overture* (Q881077), ©1991 Edmondson & McGinty. All rights assigned Queenwood/Kjos 2002. Used with permission.

65. I've Just Come From Sydney ✓ TEST

Australian Folk Song

66. Excellence in Composition: Carnival of Venice

Italian Folk Song

▶ 1) Play the theme. 2) Add eighth notes after some of the quarter notes to compose a variation as in **59. Bingo Variations**. **Bonus:** Improvise a variation!

Terms & Symbols

tempo – speed of a piece of music
Andante – walking tempo; slower than **Moderato**
Moderato – medium tempo
Allegro – fast tempo

mp   **mezzo piano** – medium soft
mf   **mezzo forte** – medium loud

accent – emphasize the note

Andante
67. Warm-up: Lullaby
Welsh Folk Song
Andante

Allegro
68. Ezekiel Saw the Wheel — *Duet*
American Spiritual

mp, >
Moderato
69. Rhythm Time
▶ 1) Write the counting and clap the rhythm before you play. 2) Play on the note B♭ (Concert B♭).
Moderato

RHYTHM STUDIES: p. 46, #54-58

70. *Sight-Reading Challenge:* Streets of Laredo
Laredo is a city in Texas on the Mexican border.
American Folk Song
Moderato

mf
71. Skill Builder: Donkey Riding
▶ 1) Add brackets to show the phrases.
2) Add a breath mark between the phrases.
Canadian Folk Song
Moderato

72. Theme from "The Nutcracker"   ✓TEST
Tchaikovsky first studied to be a lawyer but eventually became a full-time composer thanks to the support of a wealthy patron.
Peter Ilyich Tchaikovsky (1840–1893)
Russian Composer
Andante

73. Flute Private Lesson
▶ Keep your fingers close to the keys.

MASTERING EXCELLENCE: p. 38, #3

Solo

The Good Life
Solo with Piano Accompaniment

Ryan Nowlin (b. 1978)
American Composer

In addition to his work as a composer and author, Ryan Nowlin is a music teacher, horn player, and singer.

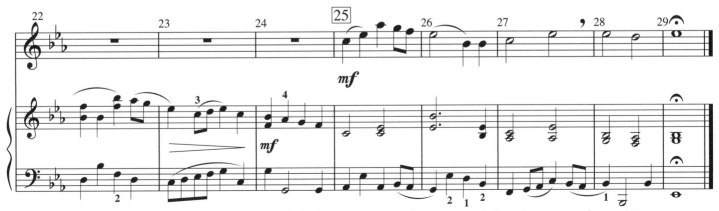

BAND PIECES

Theory & Composition	Terms & Symbols

chord – two or more notes sounded at the same time

closing – last measures of a composition, often containing music added to give a feeling of finality

long **rest** or **multiple-measure rest** – rest for the number of measures indicated

Concert Etiquette

—If you make a mistake, never let it show. Keep playing or singing as if nothing happened.
—When you are finished, graciously accept the audience's applause. Leave the stage area confidently.

chord

Warm-up: Tone, Balance, and Tuning

▶ There are many ways to perform a warm-up; follow the instructions given by your director.

closing

long rest

March Across the Seas

Bruce Pearson played clarinet and saxophone as well as baseball and hockey into his college years before becoming a music teacher, author, composer, and conductor.

Bruce Pearson (b. 1942) and
Ryan Nowlin (b. 1978)
American Composers

Procession
from "Water Music"

Water Music was written for a royal boat party on England's Thames River. The orchestra played from one barge while King George I and friends listened from another vessel close by.

George Frideric Handel (1685–1759)
English Composer
arr. Ryan Nowlin

▶ In ²⁄₄, ³⁄₄, and other time signatures, ▬ indicates a full measure of rest.

21

W61FL

Terms & Symbols

crescendo – gradually louder
decrescendo – gradually softer

natural – cancels a flat (♭) or sharp (♯)

Notes

A flat (A♭)

divisi (div.) – some performers play or sing the top notes while others play or sing the bottom notes

unisono (unis.) – everyone plays or sings the same notes

74. Warm-up: "Werde munter" — *Duet*

Johann Schop was a virtuoso violinist but also played cornet and trombone. This melody by Schop was used by J.S. Bach in his famous Cantata 147.

Johann Schop (1590–1667)
German Composer

Andante

75. Fais Dodo

▶ For lower notes, make your lip opening larger and direct your air stream lower.

French Folk Song

Andante

76. Baroque March

Though considered an English composer, Handel was born in Germany.

George Frideric Handel (1685–1759)
English Composer

Moderato

77. La Bamba

▶ Circle the notes changed by the key signature.

Mexican Folk Song

divisi, unisono, ♮

Allegro

78. Skill Builder ✔ TEST

Moderato

79. Flute Private Lesson

▶ Increase the tempo each time you practice this exercise.
Learning these fingering patterns is important to your progress.

MASTERING EXCELLENCE: p. 38, #4

Ashley

Erie Canal

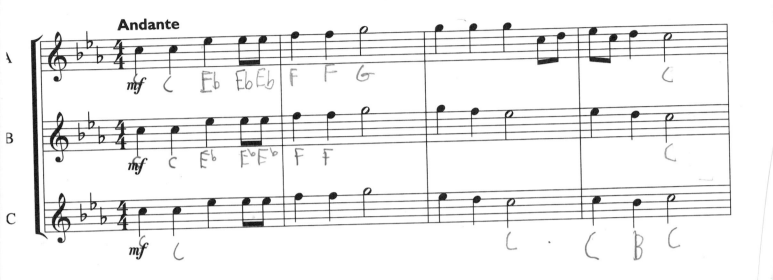

Terms & Symbols	Key Signature	Notes

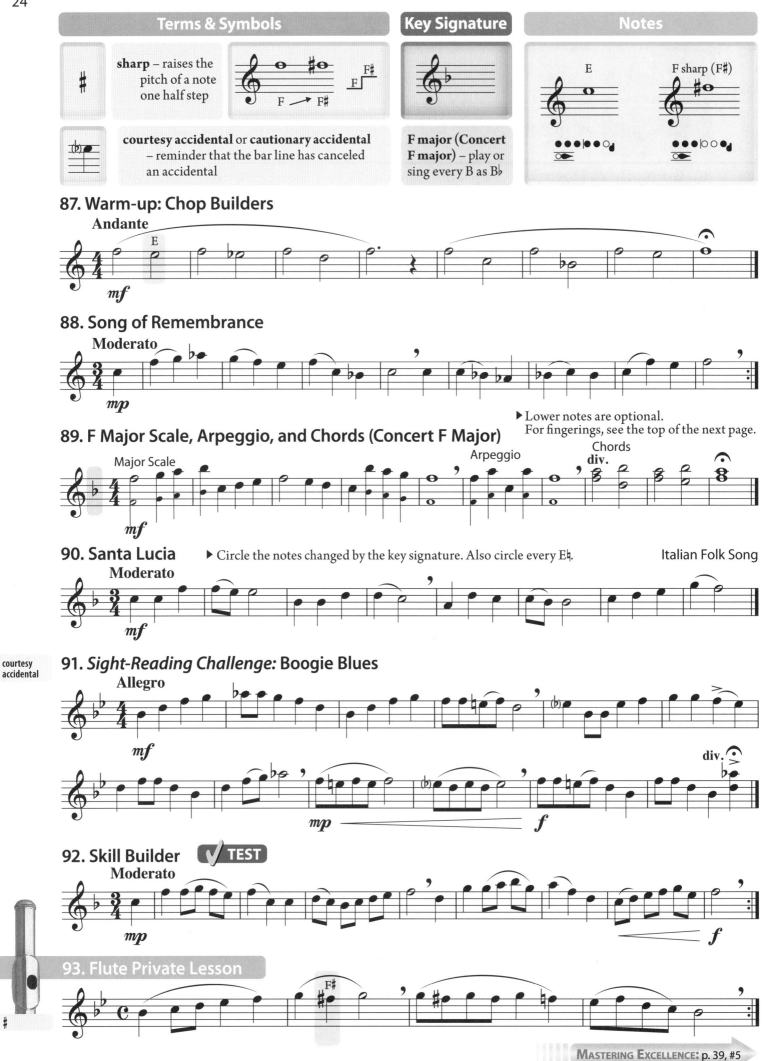

sharp – raises the pitch of a note one half step

courtesy accidental or **cautionary accidental** – reminder that the bar line has canceled an accidental

F major (Concert F major) – play or sing every B as B♭

87. Warm-up: Chop Builders
Andante

88. Song of Remembrance
Moderato

▶ Lower notes are optional.
For fingerings, see the top of the next page.

89. F Major Scale, Arpeggio, and Chords (Concert F Major)
Major Scale   Arpeggio   Chords **div.**

90. Santa Lucia   ▶ Circle the notes changed by the key signature. Also circle every E♮.   Italian Folk Song
Moderato

91. *Sight-Reading Challenge:* Boogie Blues
Allegro

courtesy accidental

92. Skill Builder   ✓ TEST
Moderato

93. Flute Private Lesson

MASTERING EXCELLENCE: p. 39, #5

W61FL

25

W61FL

Rhythm ♩. ♪

dotted quarter note = 1½ counts of sound in ²/₄, ³/₄, ⁴/₄, or ¢

COUNTING & CONDUCTING

counting	1	&	2	&
other counting				

Terms & Symbols

Da Capo al Fine (D.C. al Fine) – go back to the beginning of the piece and play or sing until the ***Fine***

Notes

D   B flat (B♭)   B flat (B♭)

alternate   alternate

101. Warm-up: Chop Builders
Andante

102. Low Down
▸ For lower notes, make your lip opening larger and direct your air stream lower.
Andante

103. Dotted Quarters
♩. ♪
▸ The bottom line provides the basic pulse.
Moderato

Clap

RHYTHM STUDIES: p. 45, #36–40; p. 46, #47–48, 59–60

104. Alouette
D.C. al Fine
▸ Orchestrate by writing in the instruments that will play each four-measure section.

French Canadian Folk Song

Allegro   *Fine*

Orchestration: _____

D.C. al Fine

105. Ronde   ✓ TEST
Moderato

Tielman Susato was a Renaissance composer, trumpet player, and music publisher. He wrote mostly dance music, including Ronde.

Tielman Susato (c. 1500–c. 1562)
Flemish (Belgian) Composer

106. Flute Private Lesson
▸ Use the alternate or thumb B♭ fingering on notes with *. Leave your thumb in this position for the entire exercise for any note requiring the thumb.

A

B

MASTERING EXCELLENCE: p. 39, #6

Maestoso – majestically

107. Soar!

Andante

108. Skill Builder

Moderato

109. *Sight-Reading Challenge:* Theme from "The Red Balloon"

Anne McGinty (b. 1945)
American Composer

Moderato

From *The Red Balloon* (Q882119), ©1993 Edmondson & McGinty. All rights assigned Queenwood/Kjos 2002. Used with permission.

Maestoso

110. Trumpet Voluntary — *Duet* ✓ TEST

Trumpet Voluntary is also known as **Prince of Denmark's March** and was originally composed for harpsichord.

Jeremiah Clarke
(c. 1674–1707)
English Composer

Introduction
Maestoso

Theme

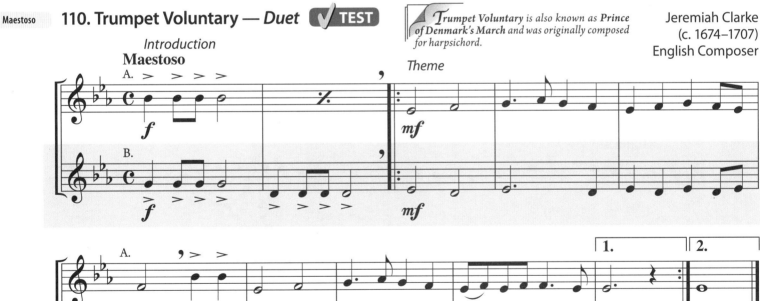

111. Excellence in Theory

▶ Add the notes and rests together to find the number of counts. A quarter note gets one count.

a)   b)   c)   d)

112. Warm-up: Range, Tone, and Tuning

Andante

113. Skill Builder

Moderato

114. Look Before You Leap

Andante

115. In the Bleak Midwinter — *Duet*

Andante

*20th Century composer Gustav Holst was a professional trombonist. **In the Bleak Midwinter** was originally written for congregational singing.*

Gustav Holst (1874–1934)
English Composer

A.

B.

116. Theme from "Symphony No. 9" ✓ TEST

Beethoven was completely deaf when he wrote Symphony No. 9 in 1824.

Ludwig van Beethoven
(1770–1827)
German Composer

Moderato

117. Flute Private Lesson

▶ 1) Write the note names. 2) Fill in the fingering chart for each note.

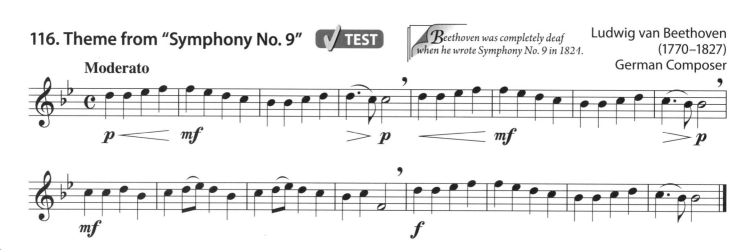

Erin Watson was born in Wichita Falls, Texas, the Lone Star State. She plays violin, piano, and accordion. She studied with famed American composer Joan Tower.

118. Lone Star Waltz

▶ 1) Orchestrate by writing in the instruments that will play each two-measure section of the music. 2) Add dynamics.

Erin A. Watson (b. 1977)
American Composer

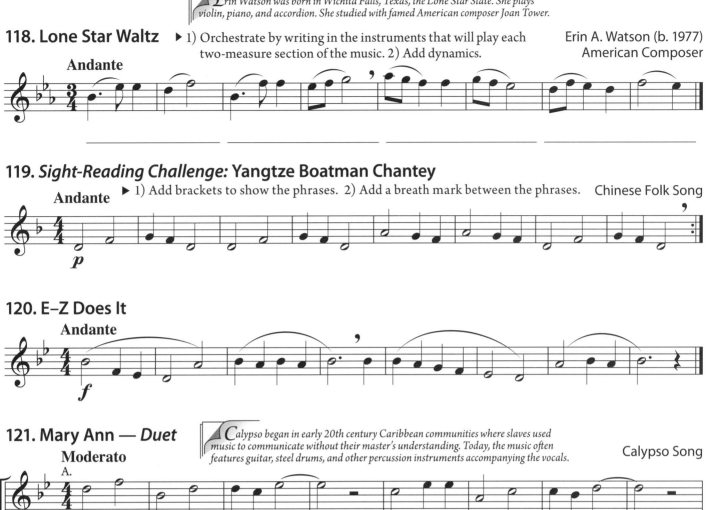

119. *Sight-Reading Challenge:* Yangtze Boatman Chantey

▶ 1) Add brackets to show the phrases. 2) Add a breath mark between the phrases.

Chinese Folk Song

120. E–Z Does It

121. Mary Ann — *Duet*

Calypso began in early 20th century Caribbean communities where slaves used music to communicate without their master's understanding. Today, the music often features guitar, steel drums, and other percussion instruments accompanying the vocals.

Calypso Song

122. Skill Builder: Happy Little Donkey — *Round* ✔ TEST

▶ Use the alternate or thumb B♭ for this entire exercise.

American Folk Song

123. Excellence in Ear Training

▶ Practice with the recorded accompaniment. Listen in measures 1, 3, 5, and 7. In measures 2, 4, 6, and 8, echo what you heard. Your starting notes are shown.

Terms & Symbols

Notes

ritardando (*ritard.* or *rit.*) – gradually slow the tempo

124. Warm-up: Chop Builders
Moderato

mf

125. Oh Yeah!
Andante

▸Use the alternate or thumb B♭ for this entire exercise.

f

126. Skill Builder
Andante

▸ Use a smooth, steady air stream. Use the alternate or thumb B♭ for this entire exercise.

f

ritardando

127. Theme from "The Sleeping Beauty"
▸ Circle the notes changed by the key signature.
Allegro

In 1891, Tchaikovsky traveled to America for the opening of Carnegie Hall in New York City.

Peter Ilyich Tchaikovsky (1840–1893)
Russian Composer

mp

f

1.

2.

rit.

mp

128. Amazing Grace ✓ TEST
Andante

American Folk Song

mp

f

mp

rit.

p

129. Flute Private Lesson

▸ For higher notes, move your jaw and lips forward and make your lip opening smaller.
For lower notes, move your jaw and lips backward and make your lip opening larger.

MASTERING EXCELLENCE: p. 39, #7

Rhythm

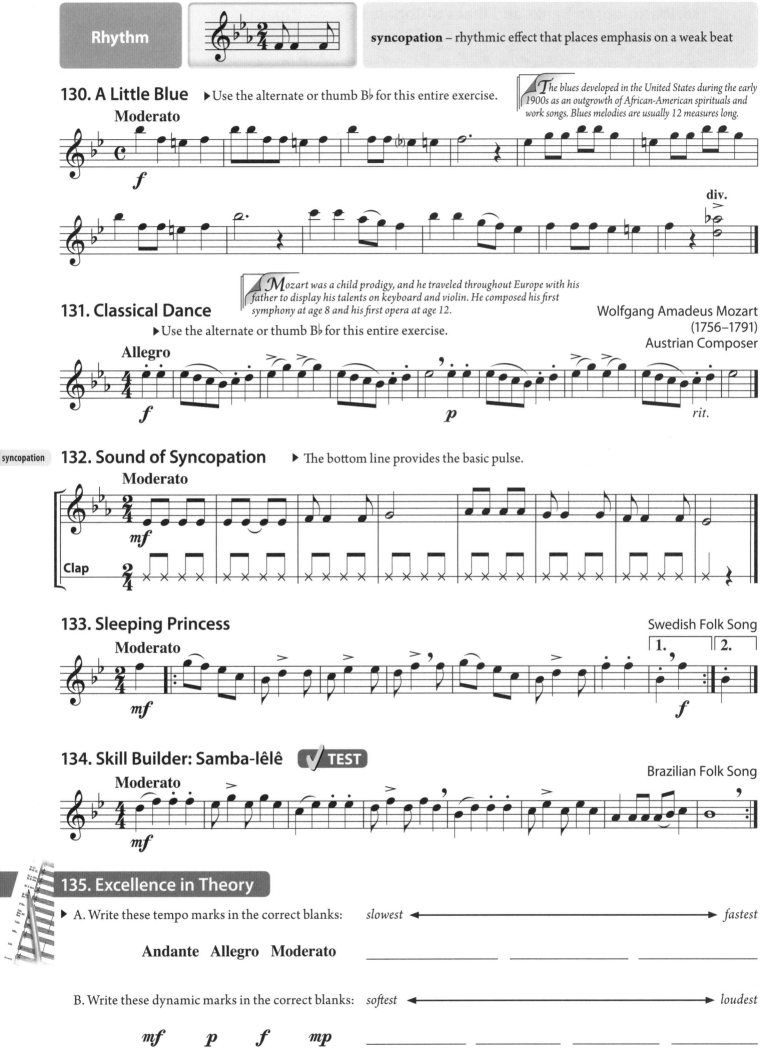

syncopation – rhythmic effect that places emphasis on a weak beat

130. A Little Blue ▶Use the alternate or thumb B♭ for this entire exercise.

The blues developed in the United States during the early 1900s as an outgrowth of African-American spirituals and work songs. Blues melodies are usually 12 measures long.

Moderato

131. Classical Dance

Mozart was a child prodigy, and he traveled throughout Europe with his father to display his talents on keyboard and violin. He composed his first symphony at age 8 and his first opera at age 12.

Wolfgang Amadeus Mozart
(1756–1791)
Austrian Composer

▶Use the alternate or thumb B♭ for this entire exercise.

Allegro

132. Sound of Syncopation ▶ The bottom line provides the basic pulse.

syncopation

Moderato

Clap

133. Sleeping Princess

Swedish Folk Song

Moderato

134. Skill Builder: Samba-lêlê ✓ TEST

Brazilian Folk Song

Moderato

135. Excellence in Theory

▶ A. Write these tempo marks in the correct blanks: *slowest* ◀─────────────▶ *fastest*

Andante Allegro Moderato   _____ _____ _____

B. Write these dynamic marks in the correct blanks: *softest* ◀─────────────▶ *loudest*

mf   *p*   *f*   *mp*   _____ _____ _____ _____

136. Warm-up: Ye Banks and Braes o' Bonnie Doon — *Duet*

Scottish Folk Song

137. Open the Door for Me! ▸ Add brackets to show the phrases.

South African Folk Song

138. Shepherd's Hey

*Australian-born composer Percy Grainger (1882-1961) is well known for his arrangements of English folk songs and country dances. His 1918 version of **Shepherd's Hey** for concert band shows Grainger's skills in orchestration, and is part of the band world's standard repertoire.*

English Folk Song

139. The Yellow Rose of Texas ▸ Use the alternate or thumb B♭ for this entire exercise.

American Folk Song

140. Manhattan Beach March ☑ TEST

Sousa played piano, violin, flute, cornet, trombone, and baritone. He is most remembered for his marches, and is known as "The March King."

John Philip Sousa
(1854–1932)
American Composer

ENSEMBLE

The term "military band" was historically used to designate an instrumental ensemble made up of woodwinds, brass, and percussion, much like today's concert band. ***Ecossaise for Military Band*** was originally written by Beethoven in 1810 for this type of ensemble. The work is a **contradance**, a lively dance-inspired composition in ²⁄₄. In a contradance, couples faced each other in two lines. It was a Classical Period predecessor to more modern forms such as square dancing.

Solo: A   **Duet:** A + B   **Trio** or **Full Band:** A + B + C

Ecossaise for Military Band

▶ 1st x = first time through. 2nd x = second time through.

Ludwig van Beethoven (1770–1827)
German Composer
arr. Bruce Pearson

BAND PIECES

ternary form

Theory & Composition	Concert Etiquette
ternary form – music with three sections: Section A, followed by a contrasting Section B, then Section A again **trio** – third theme in a march, typically a contrasting section	Dress nicely for every performance. If no specific guidelines are given by your director, be sure to ask what is appropriate. When you look your best, the audience will more fully appreciate your playing or singing.

See, the Conquering Hero Comes
from "Judas Maccabaeus"

Judas Maccabaeus, composed in 1746, is one of Handel's most famous oratorios. This piece majestically commemorates the title character's victorious return from battle.

George Frideric Handel (1685–1759)
English Composer
arr. Ryan Nowlin

Riverside March

Ryan Nowlin (b. 1978)
American Composer

▶ Notice the key signature changes at 27 and 47.

trio

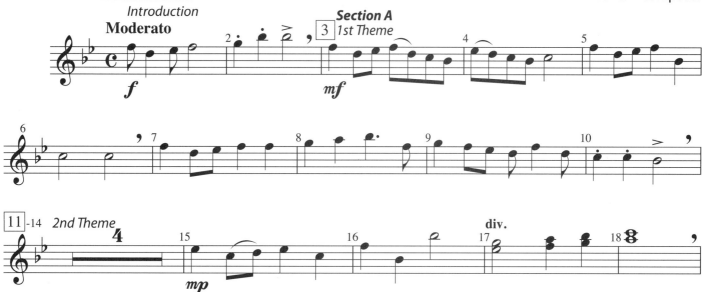

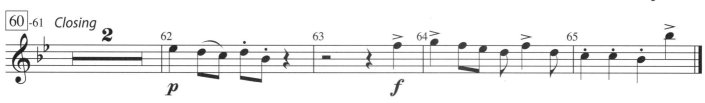

W61FL

*The **sonatina** is a form that became popular during music history's Classical Period. Between statements of the theme, it has a short development section, where the theme evolves. A large-scale version of sonatina form is sonata form.*

▶ Consider using the thumb B♭ for this entire solo. Remember you can leave your thumb in this position for any note requiring the thumb.

Sonatina
Solo with Piano Accompaniment

Albert Biehl (1836-1899)
German Composer
arr. Bruce Pearson and Ryan Nowlin

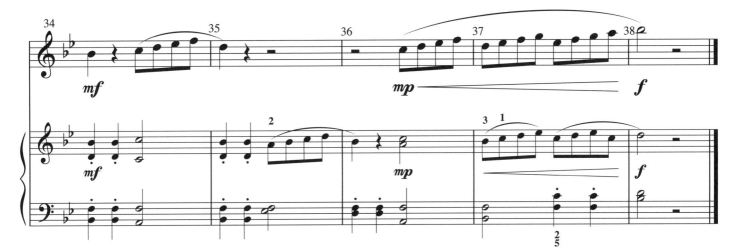

MASTERING EXCELLENCE

5. After page 24, #93

Basic Preparatory Exercise

Advanced Preparatory Exercise

Mastering Excellence

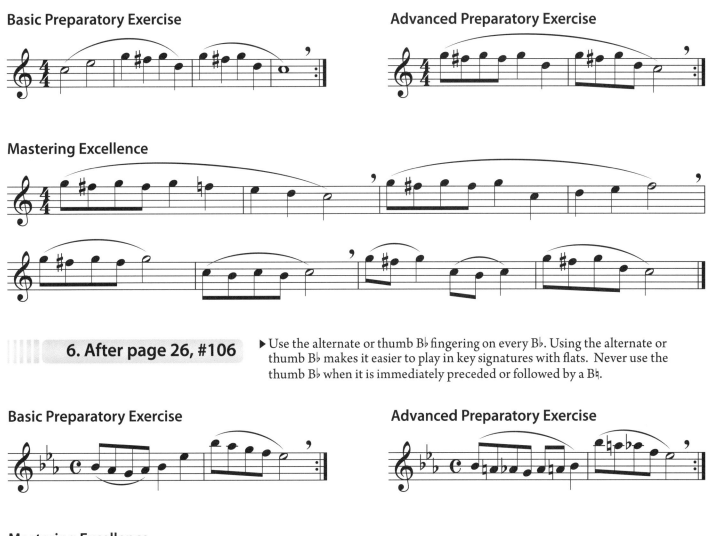

6. After page 26, #106

▶ Use the alternate or thumb B♭ fingering on every B♭. Using the alternate or thumb B♭ makes it easier to play in key signatures with flats. Never use the thumb B♭ when it is immediately preceded or followed by a B♮.

Basic Preparatory Exercise

Advanced Preparatory Exercise

Mastering Excellence

7. After page 30, #129

▶ For higher notes, move your jaw and lips forward and make your lip opening smaller. For lower notes, move your jaw and lips backward and make your lip opening larger.

Basic Preparatory Exercise

Advanced Preparatory Exercise

Mastering Excellence

Chop Builders

▶ Mix and match exercises 1A, 2A, and 3A in any combination.

1A.

2A.

3A.

1B, 2B, 3B.   ▶ Use this line to accompany 1A, 2A, and 3A.

4. Match and Pass That Note

▶ Also play with other articulations:

5. Dynamic Control

Concert B♭ Major Warm-Up

▶ Consider using the thumb B♭ for these exercises. Remember you can leave your thumb in this position
  for any note requiring the thumb.

1. B♭ Major Scale and Arpeggios

Major Scale   Arpeggios

2. B♭ Major Technique Study

▶ Also play with other articulations: A)   B)   C)

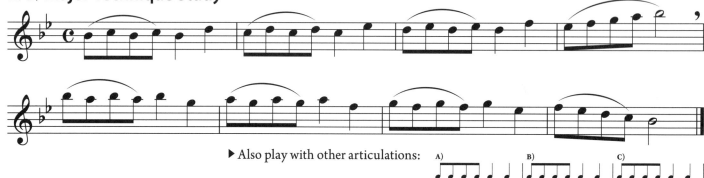

3. B♭ Major Balance and Tuning Study

4. B♭ Major Chorale: All Grace and Thanksgiving

Ryan Nowlin (b. 1978)
American Composer

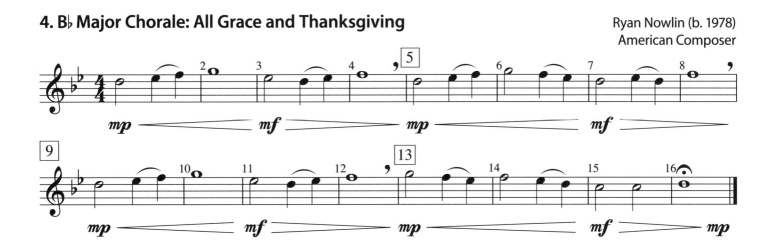

Concert E♭ Major Warm-Up

1. E♭ Major Scale and Arpeggios

2. E♭ Major Technique Study

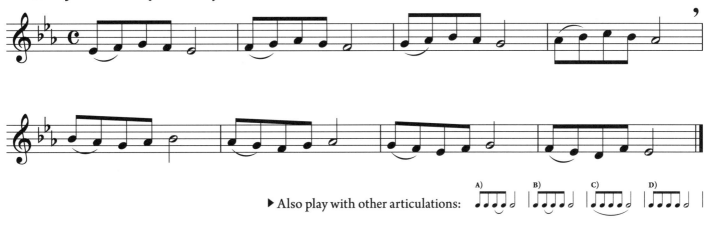

▶ Also play with other articulations:

3. E♭ Major Balance and Tuning Study

4. E♭ Major Chorale: Make a Joyful Sound

Ryan Nowlin (b. 1978)
American Composer

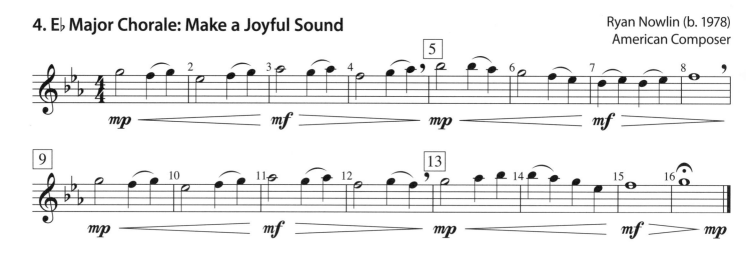

Concert F Major Warm-Up

1. F Major Scale and Arpeggios

2. F Major Technique Study

▶ Also play with other articulations:

3. F Major Balance and Tuning Study

4. F Major Chorale: Celebration and Honor

Ryan Nowlin (b. 1978)
American Composer

SCALE STUDIES

Theory & Composition   **chromatic scale** – series of 12 ascending or descending half steps

▶ For notes you do not know, refer to the fingering chart.

1. Concert B♭ Major Scale, Arpeggios, and Thirds

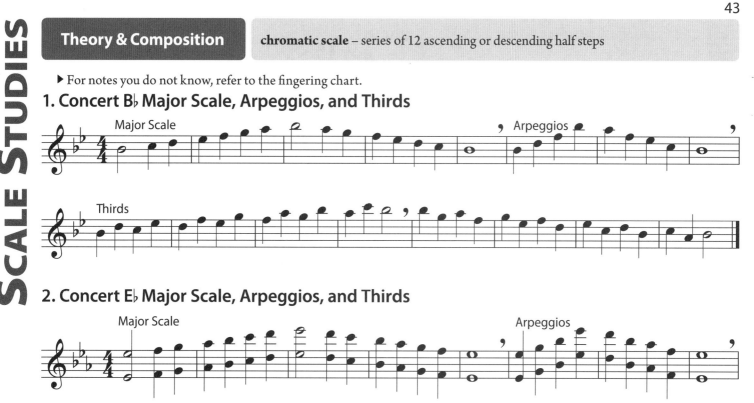

2. Concert E♭ Major Scale, Arpeggios, and Thirds

3. Concert F Major Scale, Arpeggios, and Thirds

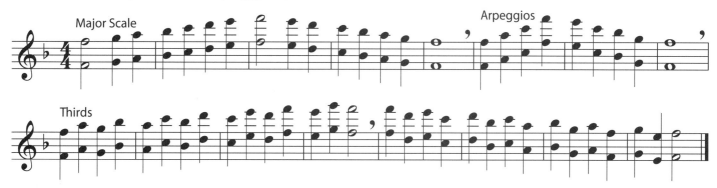

4. Concert A♭ Major Scale, Arpeggios, and Thirds

chromatic scale

5. Chromatic Scale

W61FL

RHYTHM STUDIES

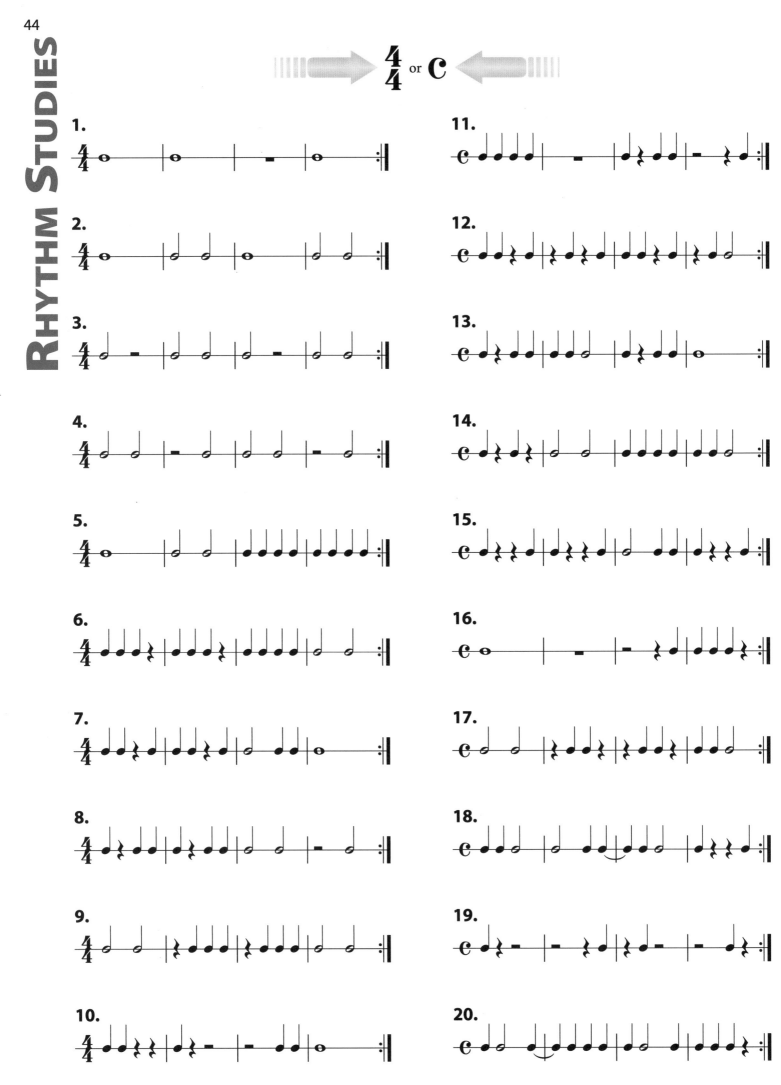

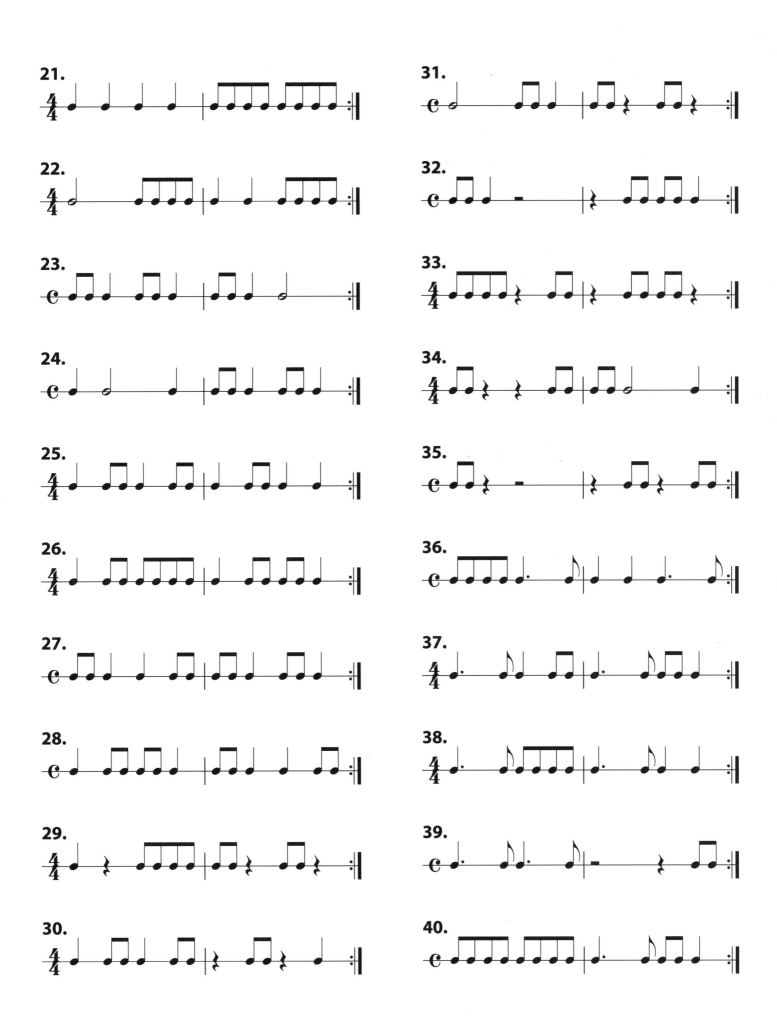

47

World Map

RESOURCES

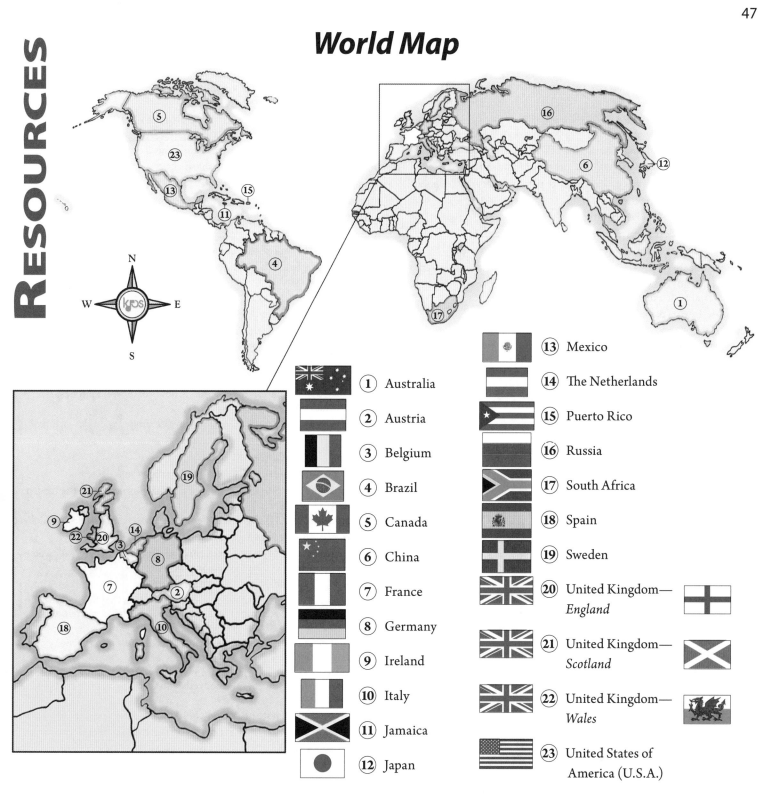

① Australia	⑬ Mexico
② Austria	⑭ The Netherlands
③ Belgium	⑮ Puerto Rico
④ Brazil	⑯ Russia
⑤ Canada	⑰ South Africa
⑥ China	⑱ Spain
⑦ France	⑲ Sweden
⑧ Germany	⑳ United Kingdom—*England*
⑨ Ireland	㉑ United Kingdom—*Scotland*
⑩ Italy	㉒ United Kingdom—*Wales*
⑪ Jamaica	㉓ United States of America (U.S.A.)
⑫ Japan	

About the Flute

The flute, originating in Central Asia, is thought by most historians to be one of the oldest musical instruments. Some early flutes were held in front of the musician, like the recorder, but the first evidence of a transverse flute (a flute held horizontally) is represented in artwork from as far back as 200 BCE. In the 12th century, the flute became commonly used in Germany, and it was most popular in military music.

Originally, flutes had only tone holes, developing from two to seven. The addition of one key for the little finger was introduced in the Baroque flute, which was built with three sections rather than only one, during the late 1600s. Theobald Boehm completely redesigned the flute in 1847 to include a key system. The Boehm system improved intonation, increased tone volume, and made notes easier to play. The modern flute is basically unchanged from this 19th century version.

Many contemporary groups use flutes: concert bands, orchestras, woodwind ensembles, chamber ensembles, and jazz bands. The common members of the flute family include the piccolo, flute, alto flute, bass flute, and contrabass flute.

FUN FACTS

▶ Many jazz and rock flutists can sing or hum while they play the flute, creating a harmony for the melodic instrument.

▶ Nose flutes are popular in some countries. They are played with air from the nose, rather than from the mouth.

▶ Check out these flutists: James Galway, Anne Drummond, Julius Baker, Sharon Bezaly, and Manuela Wiesler.

W61FL

Glossary/Index

accent – (p. 18) emphasize the note

accidental – (p. 5-6) symbol that alters the pitch of a note until the end of the measure

Allegro – (p. 18) fast tempo

anacrusis – (p. 16) see **pick-up**

Andante – (p. 18) walking tempo; slower than **Moderato**

arpeggio – (p. 23) notes of a chord sounded one after another

articulation – (p. 10) type of attack used to play a note or group of notes

bar line – (pp. 4-6) divides the staff into measures

breath mark – (p. 7) take a breath

cautionary accidental – (p. 24) see **courtesy accidental**

chord – (p. 20) two or more notes sounded at the same time

chromatic scale – (p. 43) scale of 12 ascending or descending half steps

closing – (p. 20) last measures of a composition, often containing new material added to give a feeling of finality

common time – (p. 9) means the same as $\frac{4}{4}$

composition – (p. 9) creation of music that can be performed later, usually from written notation

courtesy accidental – (p. 24) reminder that the bar line has canceled an accidental

crescendo – (p. 22) gradually louder

Da Capo al Fine (**D.C. al Fine**) – (p. 26) go back to the beginning of the piece and play or sing until the *Fine*

decrescendo – (p. 22) gradually softer

Divisi (**div.**) – (p. 22) some performers play or sing the top notes while others play or sing the bottom notes

dominant – (p. 20) fifth note of a scale; chord built on the fifth note of a scale

duet – (p. 7) piece of music featuring two different parts played or sung together

dynamics – (p. 17) softness or loudness of a piece of music

embouchure – (p. 3) mouth formation used to play an instrument

fermata – (p. 12) hold a note or rest longer than its usual value

final double bar line – (pp. 4-6) marks the end of the music

1st and 2nd endings – (p. 12) play or sing the 1st ending the first time through, repeat, skip the 1st ending, and play or sing the 2nd ending

flat – (p. 5-6) lowers the pitch of a note one half step

forte (*f*) – (p. 17) loud

G clef – (pp. 4-6) see **treble clef**

half step – (p. 5-6) smallest interval used in Western music

harmony – (p. 7) two or more notes played or sung at the same time

improvisation – (p. 15) spontaneous composition of music through playing or singing

interval – (pp. 5-6) distance between two pitches

introduction – (p. 12) opening passage of a piece of music

key signature – (p. 11) sharps or flats placed after a clef

ledger line – (pp. 4-6) short line used for notes above or below the staff

long rest – (p. 20) rest for the number of measures indicated

Maestoso – (p. 27) majestically

major scale – (p. 23) series of whole (w) and half (h) steps in the following pattern: wwhwwwh

measure – (pp. 4-6) area between two bar lines

mezzo forte (*mf*) – (p. 18) medium loud

mezzo piano (*mp*) – (p. 18) medium soft

Moderato – (p. 18) medium tempo

multiple-measure rest – (p. 20) see **long rest**

music alphabet – (pp. 4-6) first seven letters of the alphabet; these note names are assigned to the lines and spaces of the staff

natural – (p. 22) cancels a flat or sharp

one-measure repeat sign – (p. 10) play or sing the previous measure again

orchestration – (p. 23) choice of instruments used to play the music

phrase – (p. 9) musical sentence, often 4 or 8 measures long

piano (*p*) – (p. 17) soft

pick-up – (p. 16) music that comes before the first full measure of a piece

rehearsal number – (p. 12) find important places in the music using these markers

repeat sign – (p. 9) play or sing the music again

ritardando (*ritard.* or *rit.*) – (p. 30) gradually slow the tempo

round – (p. 9) song in which the same part is played or sung by two or more groups starting at different times

sharp – (p. 24) raises the pitch of a note one half step

sight-reading – (p. 7) playing or singing a piece of music for the first time

slur – (p. 10) articulation that connects notes of *different* pitches; indicates a very smooth sound

Soli – (p. 9) a small group or section plays or sings

Solo – (p. 9) only one person plays or sings

staccato – (p. 25) shorten the note

staff – (pp. 4-6) 5 lines and 4 spaces for writing music

subdominant – (p. 20) fourth note of a scale; chord built on the fourth note of a scale

syncopation – (p. 31) rhythmic effect that places emphasis on a weak beat

tempo – (p. 18) speed of a piece of music

ternary form – (p. 34) music with three sections: Section A, followed by a contrasting Section B, then Section A again

theme – (p. 12) a melody within a piece of music

theme and variation – (p. 16) type of composition that begins with a main melody (**theme**) and continues with different versions (**variations**) of the main melody

tie – (p. 11) marking that connects notes of the *same* pitch to make one longer note

time signature – (pp. 4-6) top number tells you the number of counts per measure; bottom number tells you the type of note that gets one count

tonic – (p. 20) first note of a scale; chord built on the first note of a scale

treble clef – (pp. 4-6) the line it circles on the staff is called **G**

trio (ensemble) – (p. 12) piece of music featuring three different parts played or sung together

trio (march) – (p. 34) third theme in a march, typically a contrasting section

Tutti – (p. 9) everyone plays or sings

unisono (**unis.**) – (p. 22) everyone plays or sings the same notes

variation – (p. 16) see **theme and variation**

whole step – (p. 23) interval consisting of two half steps

Timeline

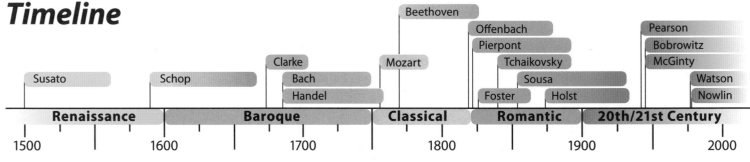